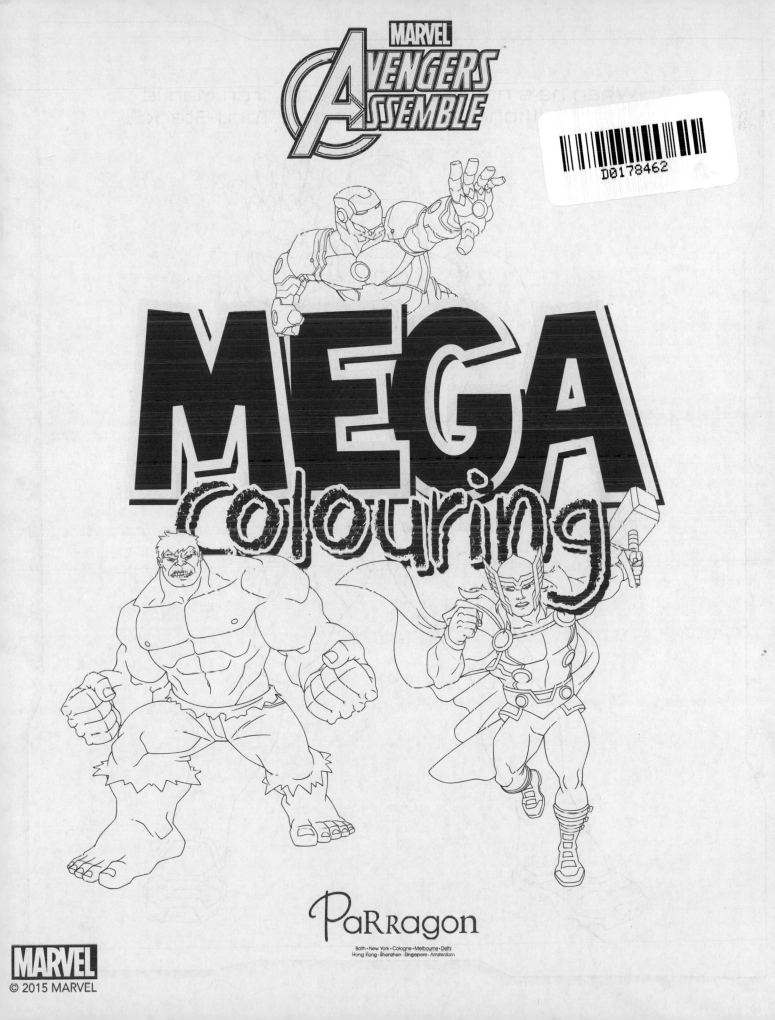

When he's not protecting Earth, Iron Man is genius billionaire businessman, Tony Stark.

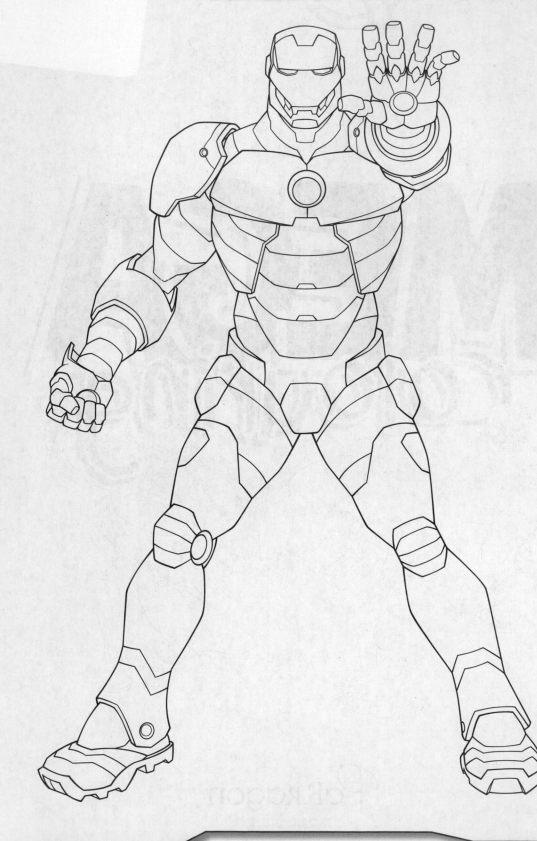

Steve Rogers became Captain America when he was given the Super-Soldier Serum during World War Two.

You wouldn't like to meet Bruce Banner
when he's angry – he turns into the Hulk!

Falcon is Tony Stark's apprentice, Sam Wilson.

Before she worked for S.H.I.E.L.D.,
Natasha Romanoff – also known as
Black Widow – was a Russian spy.

Clint Barton trained as an acrobat in the circus.
He uses these skills as Hawkeye!

Thor is from another world, known as Asgard.
He is honourable, mighty and worthy of the
power of Mjolnir, his enchanted hammer.

Before becoming director of S.H.I.E.L.D.,
Nick Fury was a highly trained soldier
in the United States Army.

S.H.I.E.L.D. stands for Strategic Homeland Intervention Enforcement and Logistics Division.

Loki is the God of Mischief. He is
determined to destroy Earth.

The Chitauri are an alien race of soldiers.

After he was exposed to a faulty version of the Super-Soldier Serum, Johann Schmidt became Red Skull.

Red Skull is the leader of HYDRA,
a group of terrorist soldiers.

Anton Vanko created the Whiplash suit
so he could battle against Iron Man.

Emil Blonsky was exposed to gamma radiation
and became Abomination. Unlike the Hulk,
he cannot change back to human form.

M.O.D.O.K. is a genius techno-criminal who can control any type of technology with his mind.

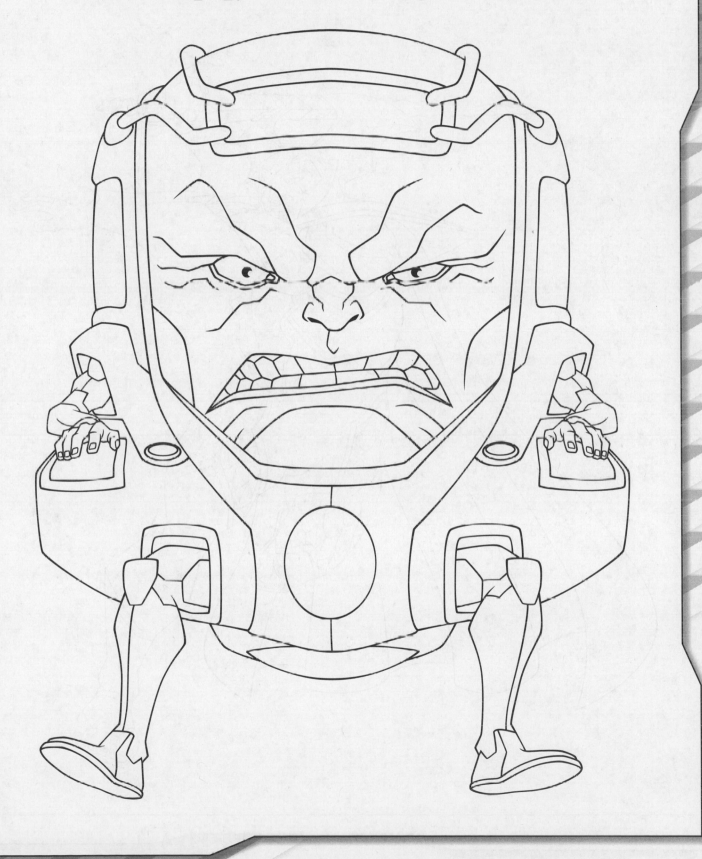

Attuma is a warlord from the underwater city known as Atlanta.

Super-adaptoid has the ability to mimic the superpowers of those around him.

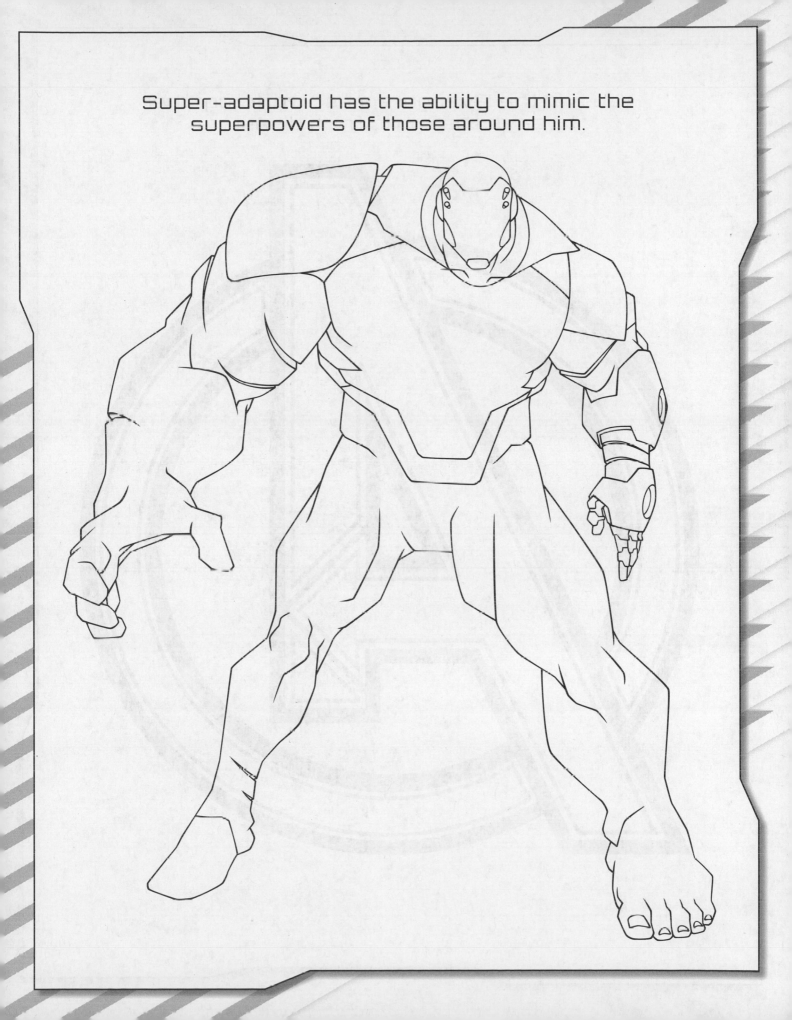

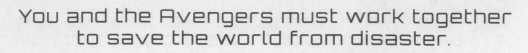

You and the Avengers must work together
to save the world from disaster.

Colour in this poster of some of the Avengers'
most fearsome enemies.

"Our enemies are gaining on us," says Nick Fury. "Time to call in the Avengers!"

The Avengers work with Fury and his
government agency, S.H.I.E.L.D.

"Time to bring the thunder!" says the Mighty Thor.

"Ready for action," says super-spy Black Widow.

"Let's fly!" yells Falcon as he soars through the air.

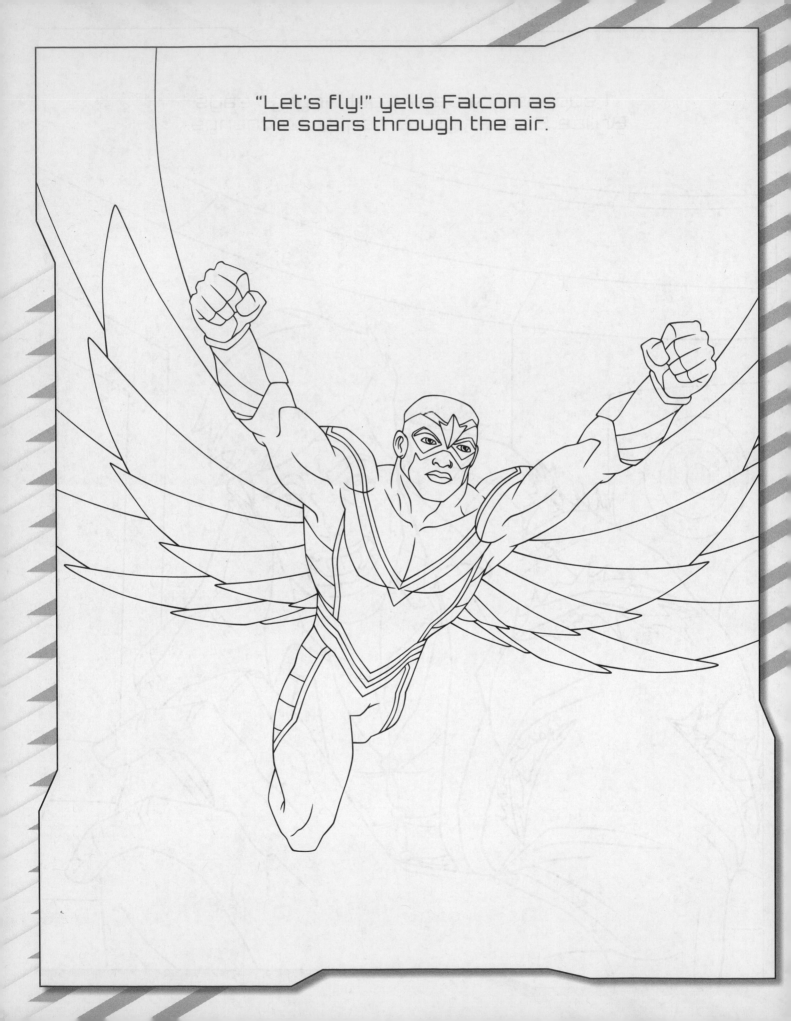

"Arrows at the ready," says Hawkeye.

"Let's fight for justice!" says Captain America.

Avengers, assemble!

"Loki has hacked into S.H.I.E.L.D.'s defence systems and stolen a top-secret weapon," Fury tells the Avengers. "We have to get it back."

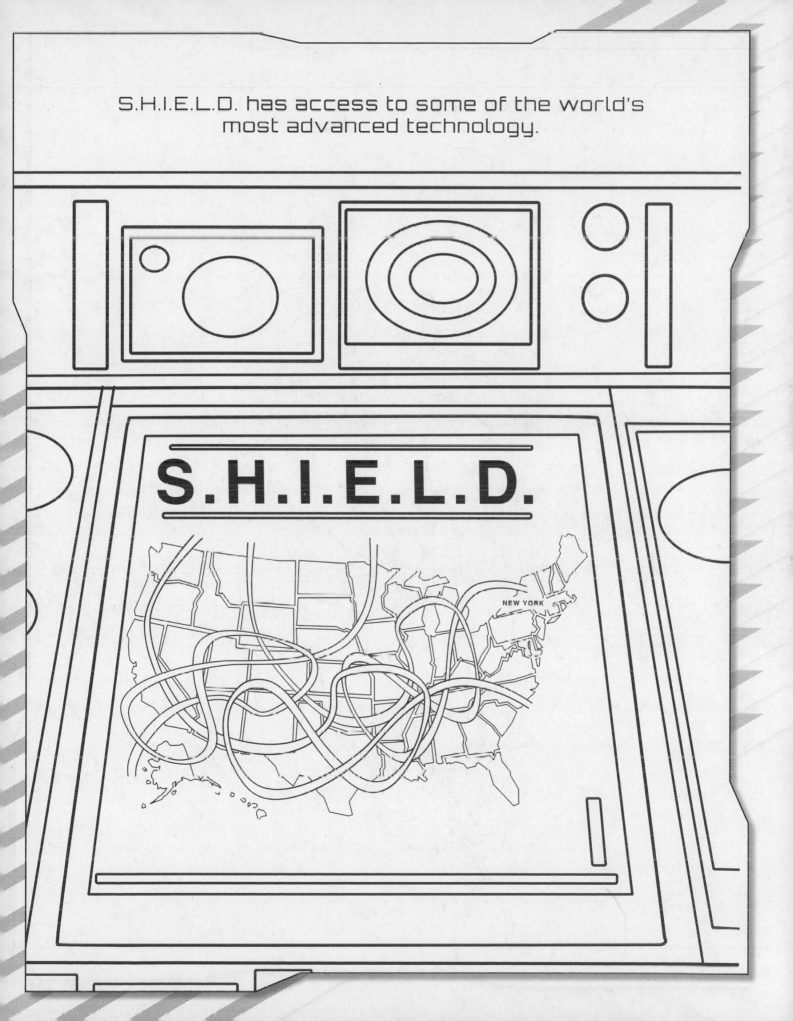

Director Fury sends Thor to
find his stepbrother, Loki.

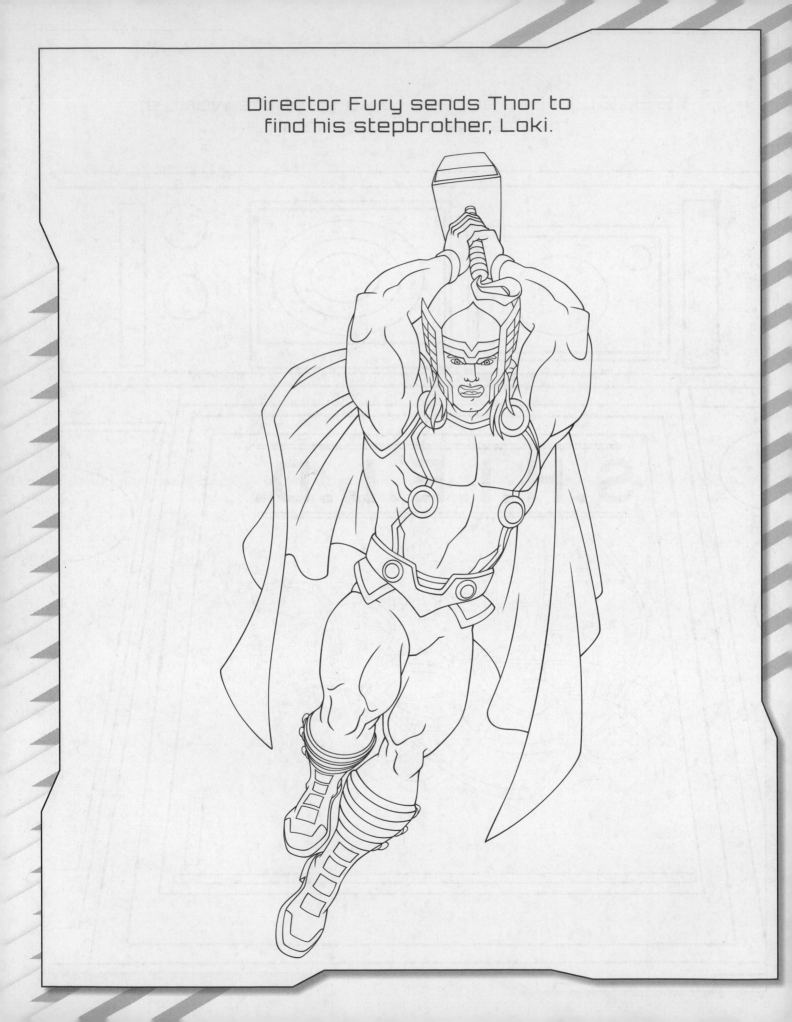

Loki believes he is the rightful king of his and Thor's home world, Asgard.

"Looks like we're keeping this in the family," says Thor when he finds Loki.

CRASH! The brothers begin to battle.

"Scared of a little lightning?" shouts Thor as he wields the power of his mighty hammer, Mjolnir.

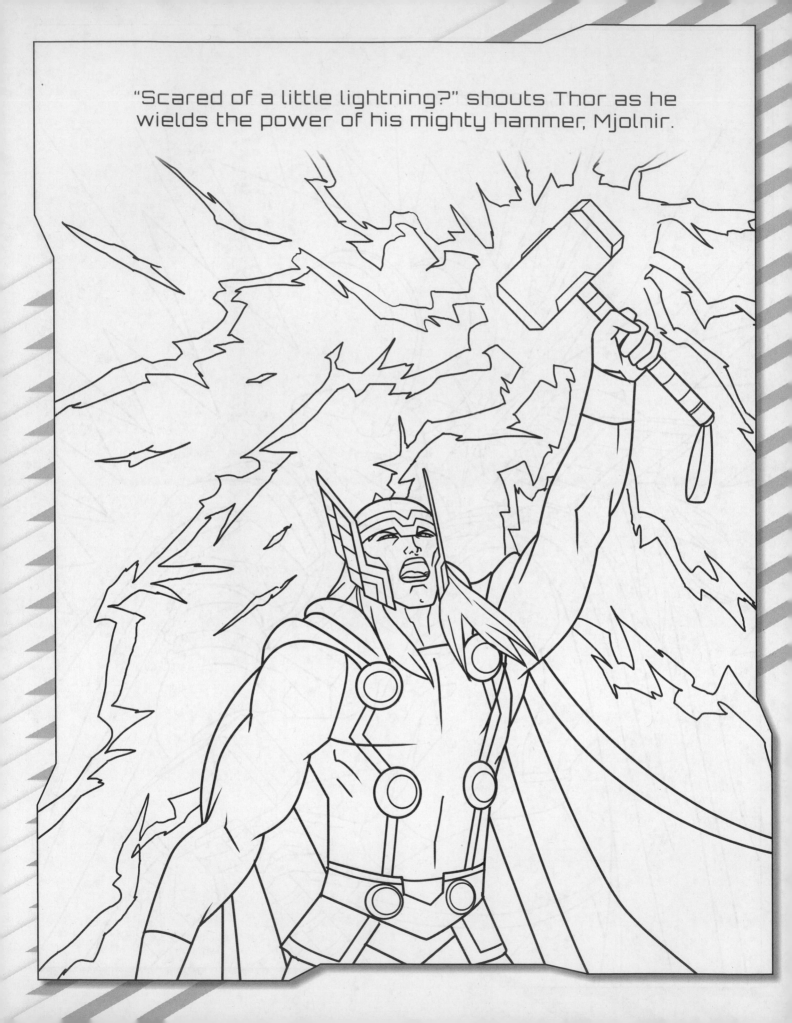

"Nothing like a bit of sibling rivalry," sneers Loki. But the God of Mischief knows he is beaten.

Loki may have lost this round, but Thor knows his brother will return.

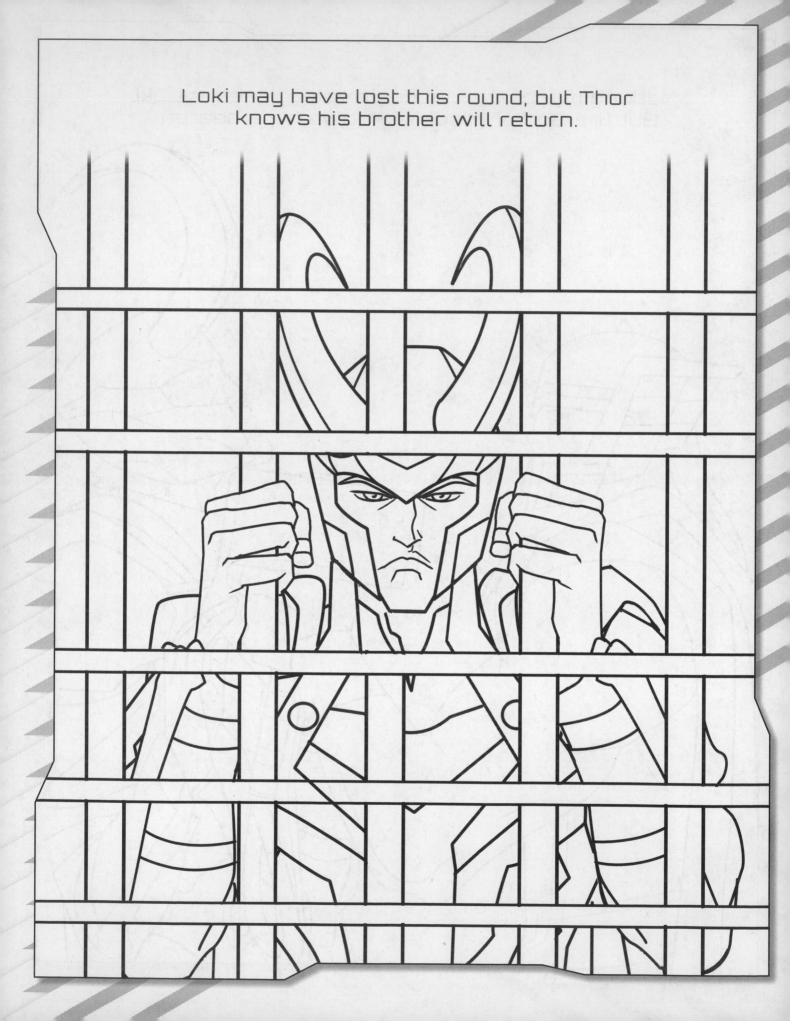

The God of Thunder wins again!

"Captain, there's been an explosion in New York City," Nick Fury tells Captain America. "Go and check it out."

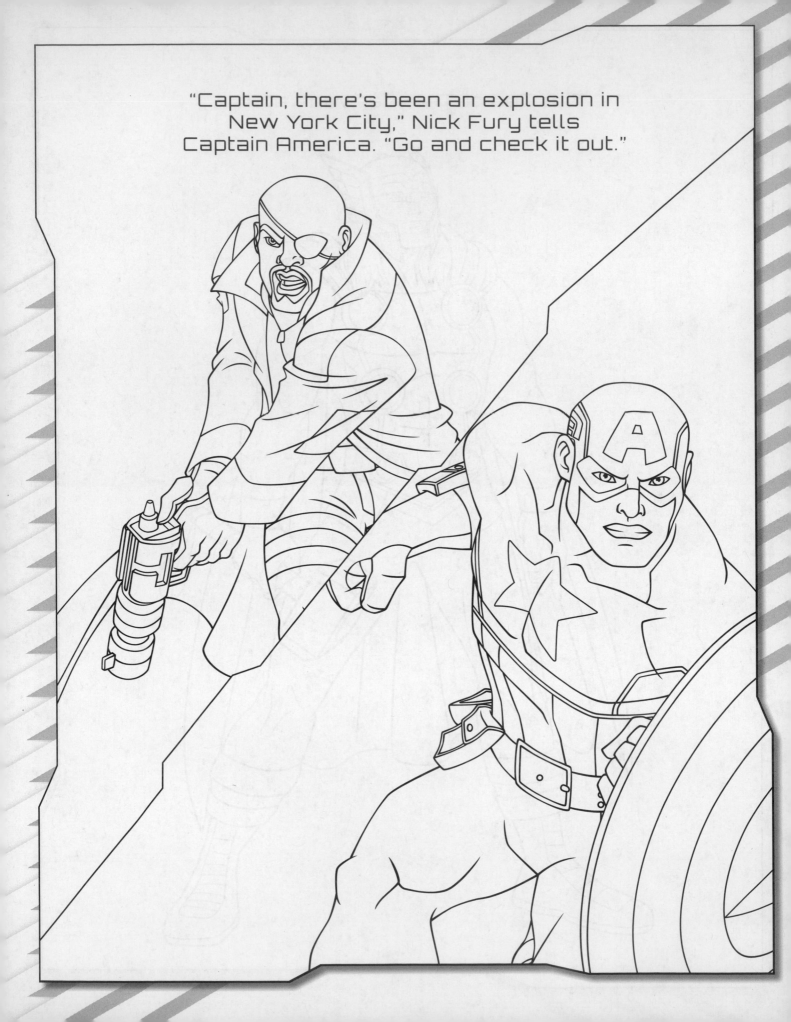

"Uh-oh. Looks like someone's causing trouble," says Captain America when he reaches the city.

Captain America speeds
towards the explosion.

Cap's oldest enemy, Red Skull, is waiting for him! Red Skull is the leader of the evil terrorist organization HYDRA.

"Time to end this, Red Skull!"
shouts Captain America.

"You wish, old man," laughs the villain.

"Need a hand ... or a wing?" asks Falcon as he soars down to join Cap.

Two Avengers are better than one.

The First Avenger throws his shield ...

... while the Winged Avenger releases his bullet-like flechettes!

"Not today, Red Skull!" shout the Super Heroes.

Red Skull is defeated! He is no match for Falcon and Captain America.

Hawkeye is a master archer. No one shoots arrows as well as him.

Black Widow is S.H.I.E.L.D.'s best super-spy.
She has a unique set of skills.

Dr Bruce Banner was just a normal guy, until he was exposed to gamma radiation and became ...

... the Incredible Hulk!

Thanos is the most feared villain
in the universe.

"Knock, knock," yells the Hulk as he crashes through a wall. "Hulk smash bad guys!"

Hawkeye swoops into action!

And Black Widow isn't far behind.

"Check out my widow's bite!" yells Black Widow, targeting the villain.

Hawkeye aims one of his explosive trick-arrows
at Thanos ...

... but Black Widow is still battling the fearsome villain and Hawkeye doesn't want to hit her by mistake!

"Hulk stop Thanos with ... HULK CLAP!" the Jade Giant shouts. The gold bars go in all directions!

But even the Hulk's booming clap isn't enough to defeat Thanos. The villain hypnotises Hawkeye and then escapes!

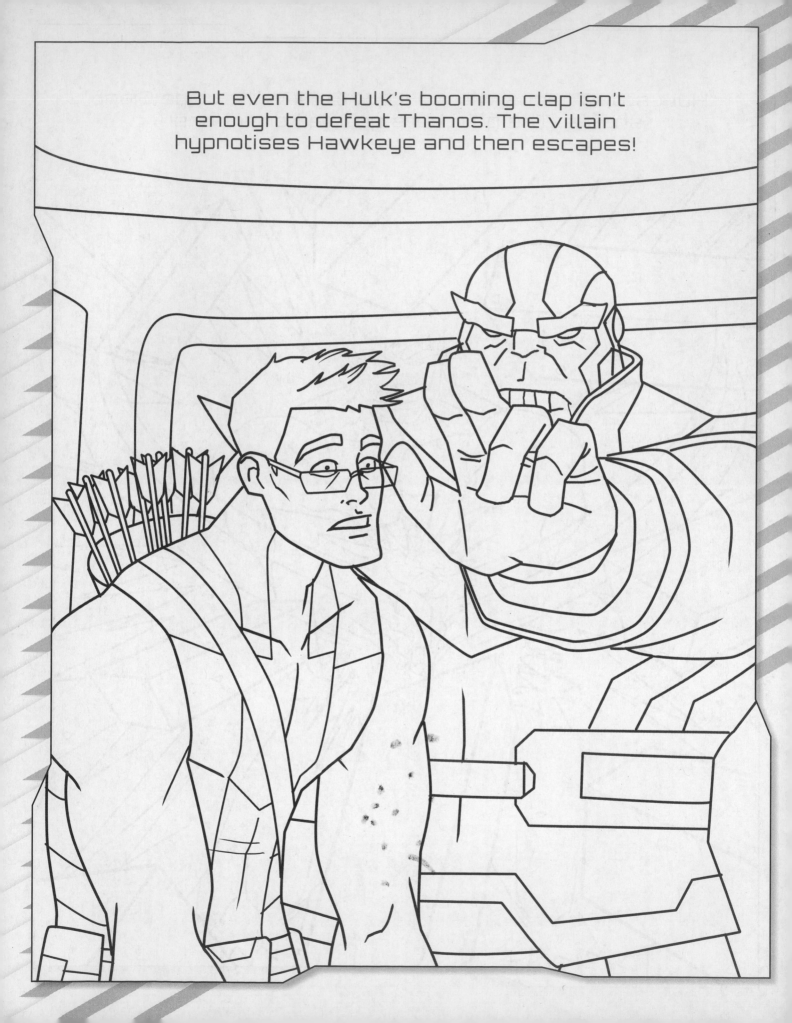

The Avengers return to S.H.I.E.L.D. headquarters,
but something's wrong with Hawkeye.

Hawkeye attacks Iron Man!

Luckily, the Armoured Avenger soon overpowers
the sharp-shooter and takes Hawkeye
for a ride to clear his head.

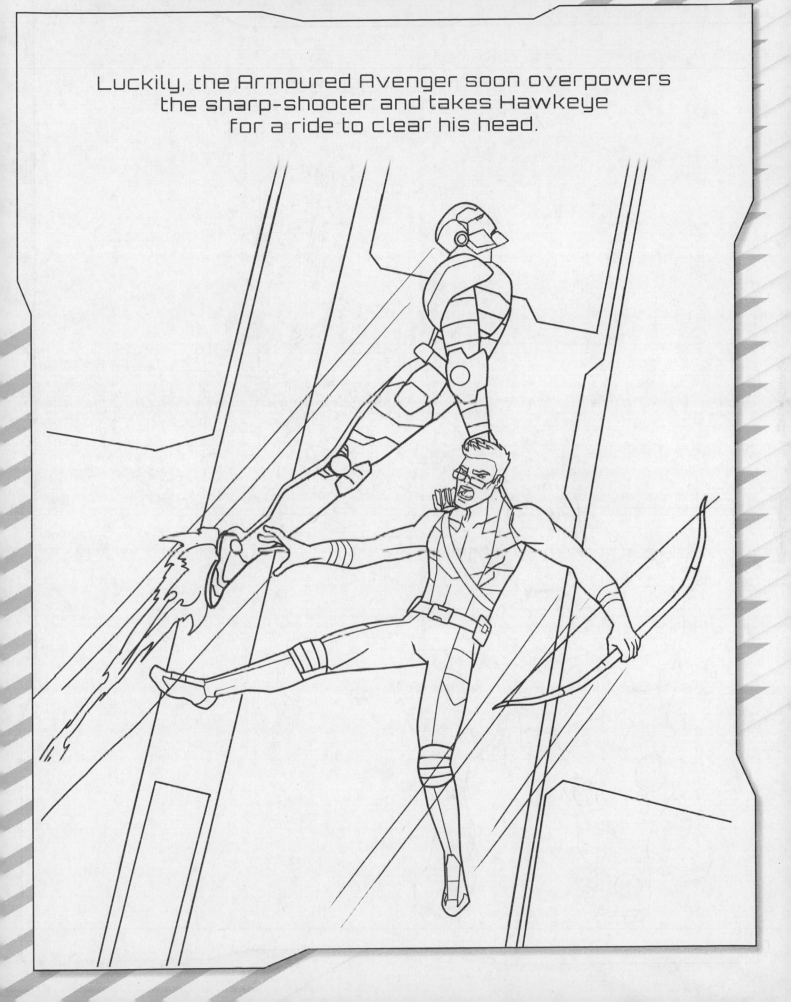

"I always thought you were a little bird-brained," Iron Man tells Hawkeye, who is feeling himself at last.

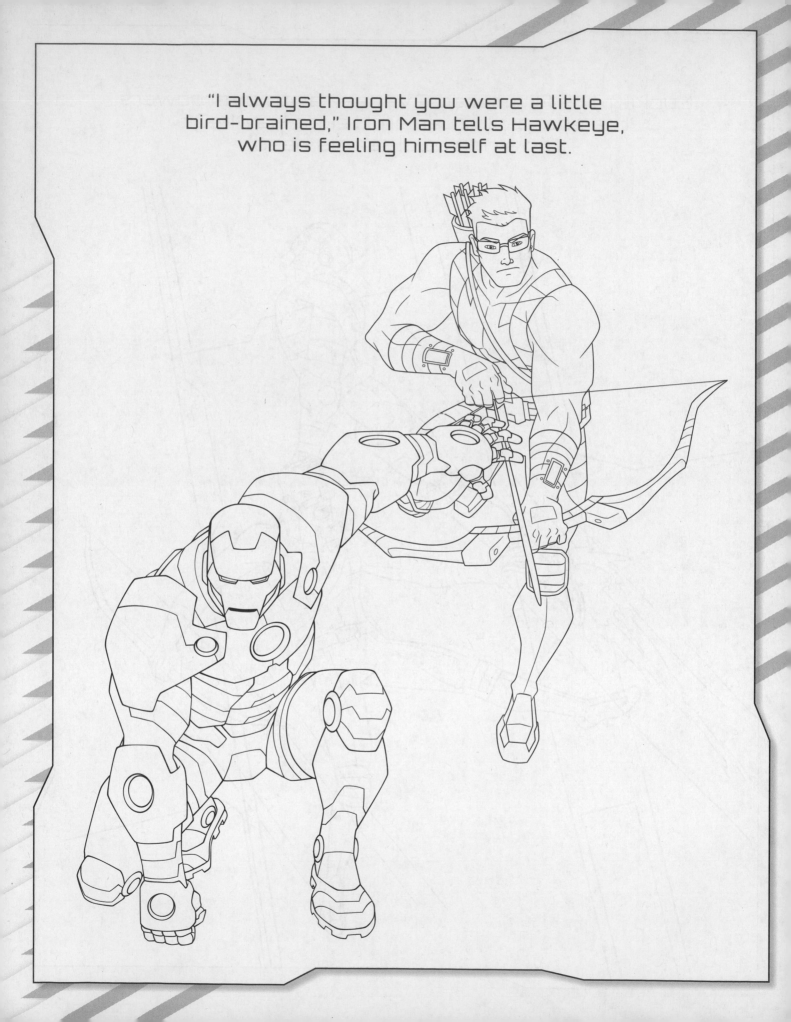

The Avengers will always protect each other.

"My systems tell me something is heading towards Earth ... and fast!" says Iron Man.

Armour up!

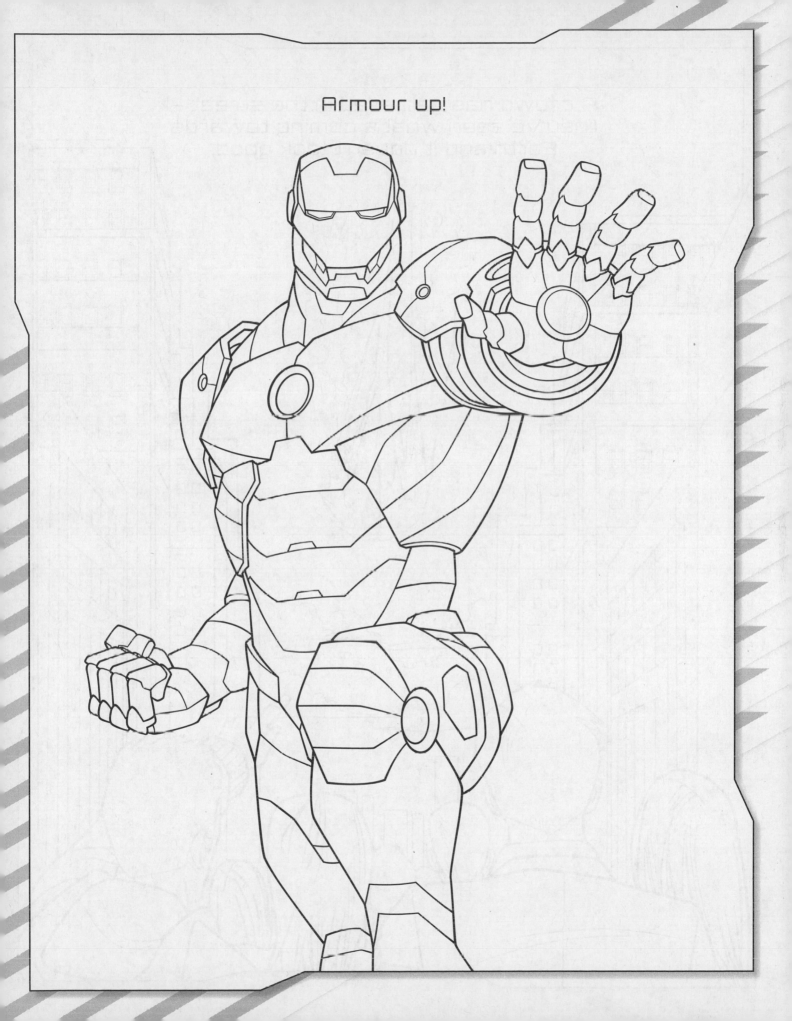

This looks like a job for Iron Man!

"This is your big break!" Iron Man shouts as he hits the comet with a repulsor blast, destroying it before it can do any harm.

Iron Man will leave no stone
unturned to keep the world safe.

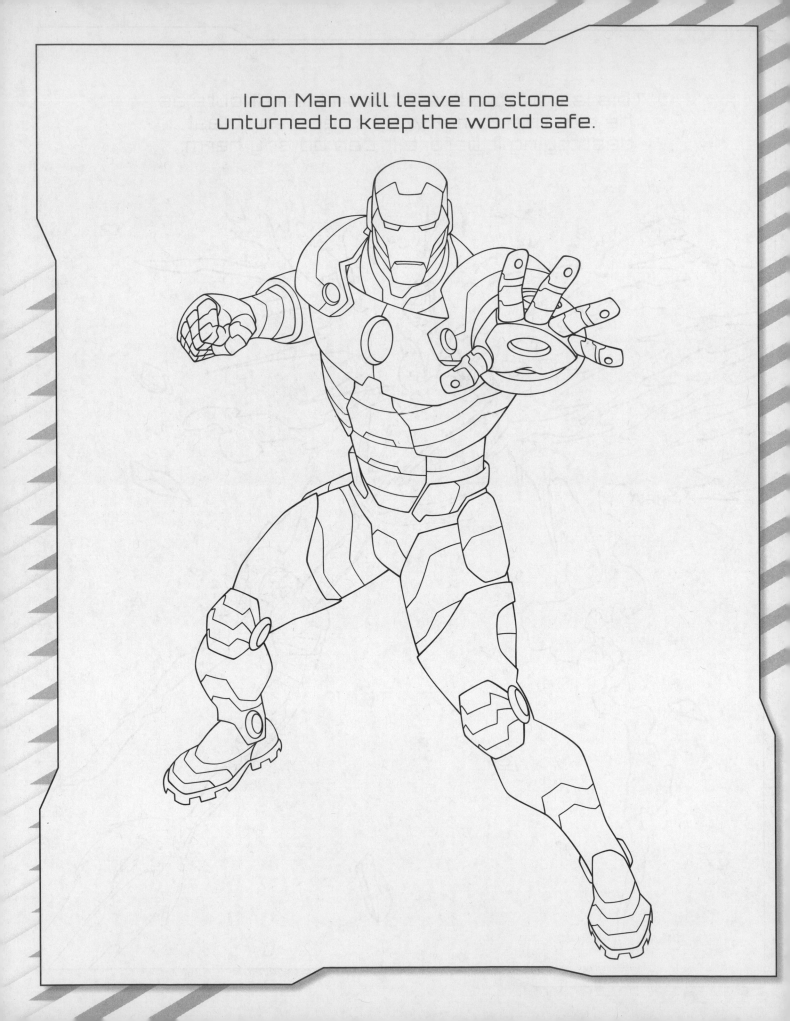

Falcon has spent the day training. "That's enough for today, Redwing," Falcon says to his bird.

"What are you up to Big Bird?" asks Iron Man.

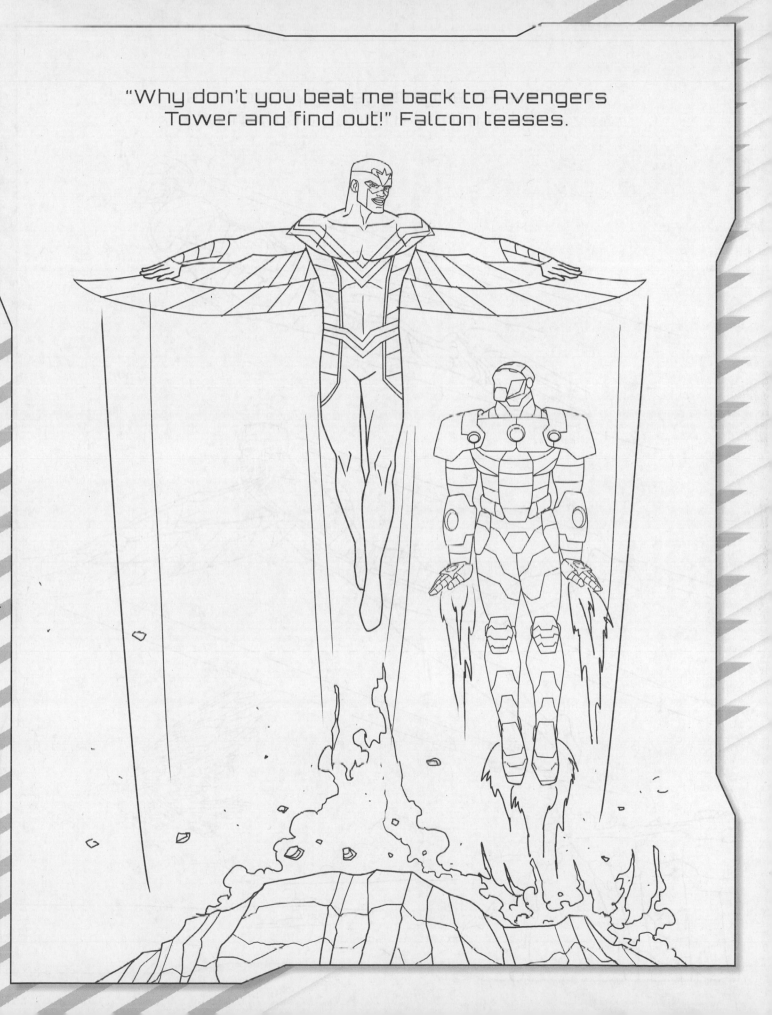

"Why don't you beat me back to Avengers Tower and find out!" Falcon teases.

The Avengers set off. Falcon is determined to beat his mentor.

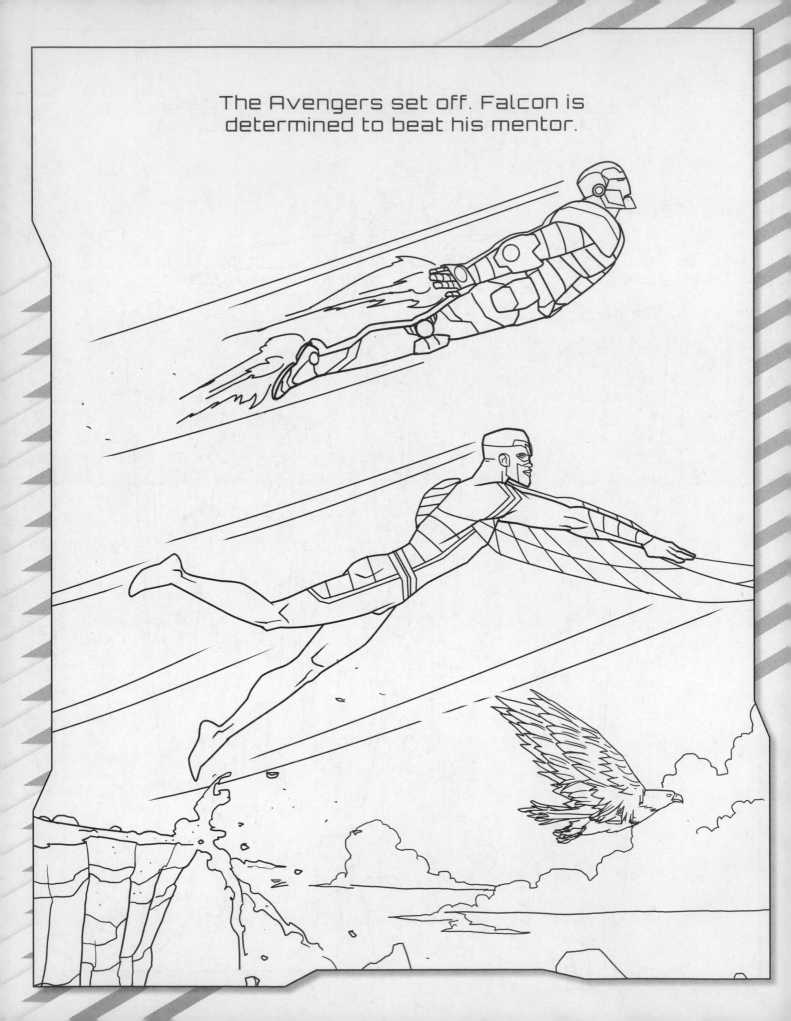

"I still have a few tricks up my sleeve!" Falcon taunts, using Redwing to distract Iron Man.

Below Falcon and Iron Man, an old enemy is testing new technology. "The changes I made to my whips will give the Avengers a surprise," Whiplash says.

Falcon flies off, but Iron Man has spotted
Whiplash and slams down to Earth.

"Today is not your day, Whiplash!"
shouts Iron Man.

"Time to play, my old friend," sneers Whiplash, cracking his whips at Iron Man.

"You're too slow, Vanko!" Iron Man shouts, taunting his foe.

"Sorry about the mess," Iron Man says to the farmer as he flies off with Whiplash.

Whiplash hangs his head. He thought his next fight
with Iron Man would be harder on the Avenger.

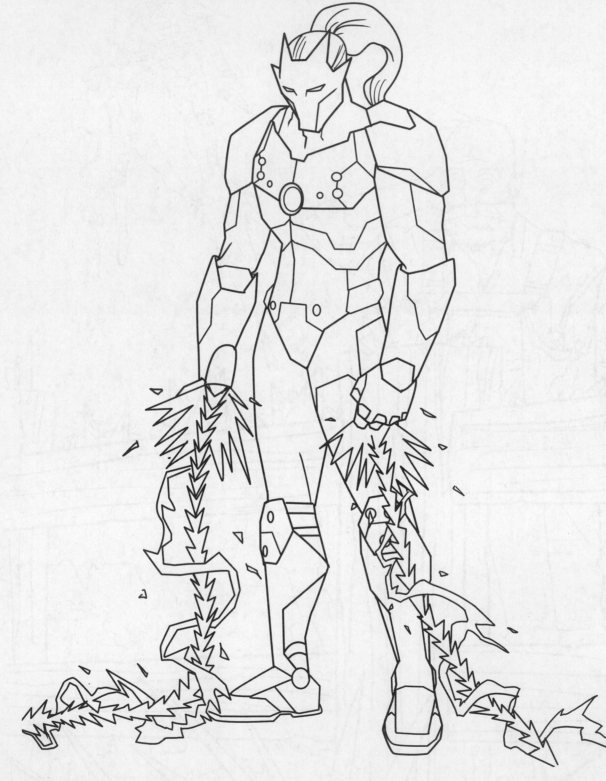

There will always be those who
try to cause trouble....

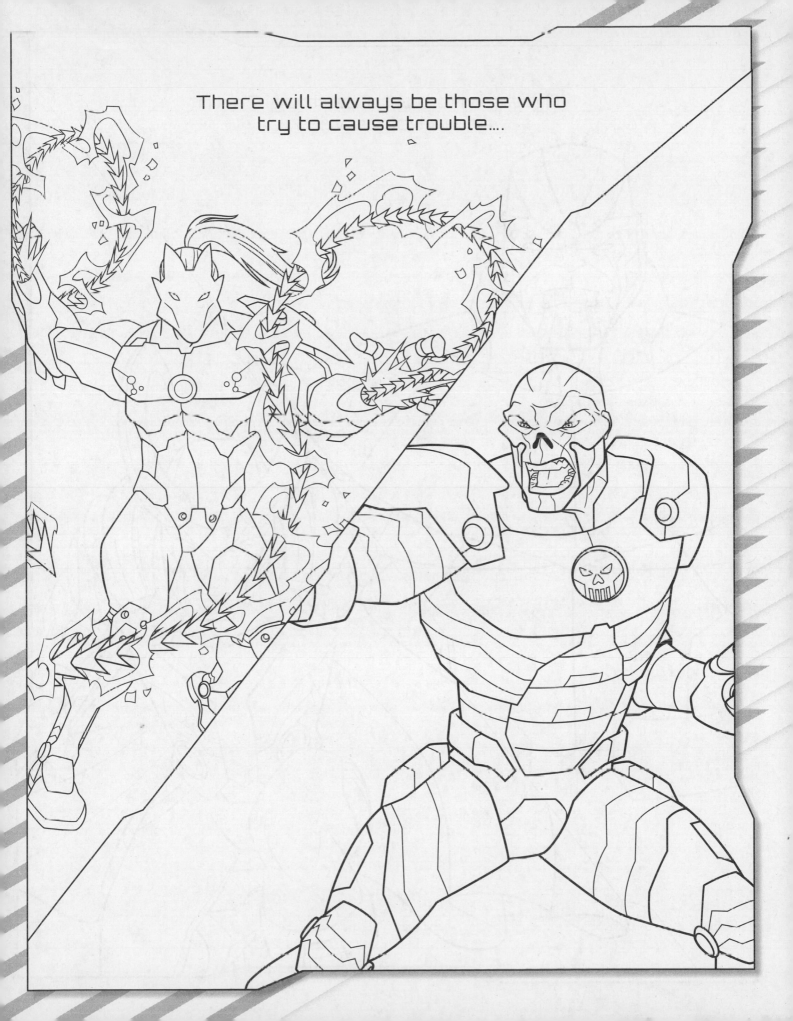

Those who try to destroy Earth
and all of us with it.

But as long as there are villains, there will be Super Heroes to protect us.

And those Super Heroes are called ...

the Avengers!